What does the Bible really say about

Eating Disorders

Emma Scrivener

"For Richard, who stood with us in the mess."

Eating Disorders
Emma Scrivener

ISBN 978-1-84625-523-6

Copyright © Day One Publications 2016

Cover design and typesetting by Dave Hewer Design (davehewer.com).

British Library Cataloguing in Publication Data available.

Scripture quotations are from The Holy Bible, English Standard Version® (ESV®), copyright © 2001 by Crossway, a publishing ministry of Good News Publishers. Used by permission. All rights reserved.

Printed by Orchard Press Cheltenham Ltd

Contents

1.

Always hungry?

And he humbled you and let you hunger and fed you with manna, which you did not know, nor did your fathers know, that he might make you know that man does not live by bread alone, but man lives by every word that comes from the mouth of the Lord.

(Deuteronomy 8:3)

How did you feel when you picked up this booklet? Perhaps the title immediately caught your attention. You're grappling with an eating disorder (ED), or know someone who is. Or maybe you find EDs hard to understand, but would like to know more. Whatever your experience, EDs affect us all. That's because they're about more than what goes in our mouths. First and foremost, they're about what's in our *hearts*. They're ways of answering life's big questions, like:

- ▷ Where do I belong?
- ▷ What makes me special?
- ▷ How can I be accepted?
- ▷ What do I do with my fears?
- ▷ Who can I trust?
- ▷ What is life all about?

You may never have struggled with food. But all of us have asked these questions — because they're part of what it is to be human. So, how do *you* respond? Some of our answers are good; like praying or talking to friends. But some are more complicated. Maybe we take our fears shopping. Maybe we drown them. Maybe we starve them. Maybe we swallow them. However we make sense of life, if our hope is in something *we* do, then we're in need of help. Let's think about why.

More than food

Everyone gets hungry. From Hollywood A-listers to the beggars of Calcutta, we all need to eat. Yet our appetites go deeper than food. We need air and water. We need shelter, covering and warmth. We have emotional needs too: for love, security,

> "...the very first eating disorder. It's a condition that affects us all, even today."

acceptance and relationship. We keep asking, "what will we do with our cravings and how can we be filled?"

To find out, let's start with the very first humans and the very first eating disorder. It's a condition that affects us all, even today.

A cosmic eating disorder

Our hungers come from God — but He meets them too. We see this with Adam and Eve in Genesis 3. God gives them good hungers and He also fills them with good things. In fact, there's no aspect of His creation that He hasn't shared, (see Genesis 2:15-25). He gives them only one rule: "Don't eat from the tree in the middle of the Garden — or you will die." But instead of being satisfied, they want more. When the serpent tempts them, they quickly disobey. Read Genesis 3:1-7 to see how.

Instead of relying upon God, Adam and Eve trust in themselves. This is much more than biting into a bad piece of fruit. It's about rejecting God and His provision. It's about wanting to be *like* Him and to take His place:

> *But the serpent said to the woman, "You will not surely die. For God knows that when you eat of it your eyes will be opened, and you will be like God, knowing good and evil."* Genesis 3:4-5

In some ways, this is the very first eating disorder. But none of us are exempt.

Key Point

God gave us good hungers so we would turn to Him, but since the Fall our appetites have become distorted.

Genesis 2-3, Psalm 78:9-39, 1 Timothy 4:1-5

2. Denying (our) dependence

> *There is nothing outside a person that by going into him can defile him...*
> *For from within, out of the heart of man, come evil thoughts...* (Mark 7:15, 21)

God warns Adam and Eve, "if you eat of the fruit you will surely die." They refuse to listen — and as a consequence, the whole world is cursed. Everything that God made good is now distorted — including our hungers. These hungers are a blessing because they invite us to rely upon God, but since the Fall, they feel like a threat. We no longer rule our appetites; instead, they rule us:

> *What causes quarrels and what causes fights among you? Is it not this, that your passions are at war*

within you? You desire and do not have, so you murder. You covet and cannot obtain, so you fight and quarrel. You do not have, because you do not ask. (James 4:1-2)

Instead of trusting in our generous Father, we're rebels and we demand our independence. We won't ask God for food, because we want to be Lord in His place. However, if we reject His provision, we must also feed ourselves. We can feast on all that the world has to offer — or deny our desires instead. We can choose to stuff our hungers — or we can try to starve them.

Stuffing

Let's start with "stuffing." This includes food — but it's much more. We try to fill ourselves with all sorts of things, from relationships and entertainment to possessions or work. These can be good in themselves, but they can't take God's place. Your job might be fulfilling, but it's not who you are. Your partner might be loving, but they can't bring you peace. If we look to these things for ultimate meaning, they'll collapse under the weight. They're good — but not good enough.

> "If we look to these things for ultimate meaning, they'll collapse under the weight."

Starving

Instead of feeding our cravings, we can deny them completely. We can close ourselves down and put our trust in self-discipline, rules and sheer willpower. Paul talks about this in Colossians 2:20-23:

> *If with Christ you died to the elemental spirits of the world, why, as if you were still alive in the world, do you submit to regulations — "Do not handle, Do not taste, Do not touch" (referring to things that all perish as they are used)—according to human precepts and teachings? These have indeed an appearance of wisdom in promoting self-made religion and*

asceticism and severity to the body, but they are of no value in stopping the indulgence of the flesh.

Rules and self-denial look wise, but they're only skin-deep. Jesus reminds us of this in Mark 7:14-23. It's not what we eat that makes us unclean; it's what's already there! Even when we change our body or our diet, we can't change the desires of our hearts. We

> "Even when we change our body or our diet, we can't change the desires of our hearts."

were made to depend upon God — but we won't give Him our desires. For some it will come out in food and EDs, but it's a problem that we all face.

In chapter three we will look at specific eating disorders. But first, let's think about hunger in a general sense. In what ways do you stuff — grasping after satisfaction that isn't wise? In what ways do you starve — denying your dependence on God for all things?

Key Point

All our hungers are versions of our hunger for God. Yet instead of depending upon Him, we look elsewhere for satisfaction. Deuteronomy 8:1-18; Deuteronomy 32:18, Psalm 145:15-16, Jeremiah 2:10-13, Matthew 4:1-4, Philippians 4:19.

3. Food and feelings

Some were fools through their sinful ways, and because of their iniquities suffered affliction; they loathed any kind of food, and they drew near to the gates of death. (Psalm 107:17-18)

All of us have disordered desires. Let's think about how they are expressed in EDs.

Who

 ▷ EDs look different, but are ways of *using food to cope with and control life.*
 ▷ The most well known are Anorexia and Bulimia but there are many more — and they don't fit in neat boxes! (See below.)
 ▷ It's estimated that of those with EDs, 10% are

anorexic, 40% are bulimic and the rest fall into the category of EDNOS (Eating Disorder Not Otherwise Specified — including Binge-Eating Disorder).

▷ They affect all ages and both men and women.

What

Anorexia: Restricting food intake sometimes combined with excessive exercise. 5% of anorexia cases are fatal, making it the most deadly mental illness.

*Typical symptoms **may** include:*

▷ Inability to maintain a minimum body weight.

▷ Disrupted periods.

▷ Missing meals, eating very little or in secret, avoiding "fattening" foods.

▷ Intense fear of becoming fat, despite being underweight.

▷ A distorted perception of their body shape.

▷ "Brain fog" - poor concentration, missing school,

college or work.
▷ Often denies any
problem.
▷ Physical
symptoms such

as constipation and stomach pains, dizzy spells and fainting, swollen stomach, face and ankles, downy hair on the body or hair loss when recovering, poor blood circulation.
▷ Personality changes, (e.g. anxiety or depression, being secretive, loss of interest in normal activities, withdrawal from others).

Bulimia: Eating large quantities of food ("binging"), then getting rid of it ("purging"), e.g. by vomiting, abusing laxatives or exercising to excess. An average bulimic binge may consist of about 1,500 to 3,000 calories, (but can go up to 60,000 calories or more).

Bulimia is the *most common ED*, (1-2% of the population are estimated to be affected).

*Symptoms **may** include:*

▷ Frequent weight changes, disappearing to the toilet after meals in order to vomit, sore throat or tooth decay, swollen salivary glands, poor skin, irregular periods and lethargy.

▷ Uncontrollable urges to eat vast amounts of food, followed by guilt and anxiety leading to purging.

▷ A distorted perception of body weight and shape, anxiety and depression, low self-esteem and feelings of isolation.

▷ A struggle with impulsive or obsessive behaviours, (e.g. food rituals, promiscuity, overspending or even shoplifting for food).

▷ Possible laxative use, periods of fasting and excessive exercise, secretive behaviour.

▷ Financial worries (due to food costs).

EDNOS: Eating Disorder Not Otherwise Specified. This is the term for EDs that don't meet the criteria for anorexia or bulimia, or are a combination of the two (e.g. a woman who is anorexic but still menstruating).

It's *the most common hospital diagnosis*. Examples include: enterophobia (fear of sickness), diabulimia (where people with Type 1 diabetes deliberately give themselves less insulin than they need), orthorexia (eating only "clean" or "healthy" foods) and binge-eating disorder.

Binge-Eating Disorder (BED): Consuming very large quantities of food over a short period of time, even when not hungry.

*Symptoms **may** include:*

- ▷ Eating an unusually large amount of food very quickly, far more than an average person would eat — but often unconsciously.
- ▷ Eating until physically uncomfortable and nauseated or when depressed or bored.
- ▷ Eating alone during periods of normal eating, because embarrassed about food.
- ▷ Feeling disgusted, depressed and guilty after binge eating.

Symptoms are similar to bulimia but those with BED do not purge, fast or over-exercise after binge eating. Whilst, bulimics are typically of normal weight, those with BED are more likely to be obese.

What causes EDs?

There's rarely a single cause, usually, it's a combination of biological, psychological and environmental factors. These include personality type, culture, life experiences or stresses, family history and even sickness.

Key Point

EDs come in different forms and affect all sorts of people.
Proverbs 25:16, Psalm 107:43, Romans 14:1-23,
1 Corinthians 10:1-13

Sources used in this chapter: http://www.b-eat.co.uk/about-beat/ media-centre/facts-and-figures/ (Aug 2014)

4. How EDs "work"

There is a way that seems right to a man, but its end is the way to death. (Proverbs 14:12)

What they do

Many sufferers don't see their ED as a problem, but as a way of dealing with other problems.

Examples:
- ▷ Communicating *dangerous feelings* — "writing on my body what I can't say with my mouth".
- ▷ Getting *rid of emotions* — transferring feelings to the physical — e.g. by physically "purging or harming myself". This temporarily relieves uncomfortable feelings and anxiety.
- ▷ Trying to "*change* myself".

- ▷ Causing a *distraction*
- ▷ To *regain control* over difficult feelings or circumstances.
- ▷ *Comfort*: For the binge-eater, food can be temporarily soothing or numbing. For the anorexic, not eating provides a feeling of security and control. For the bulimic, binging feels impulsive, whilst purging feels like a way of taking control back.
- ▷ *For self-punishment*: e.g. for having strong or "bad" feelings
- ▷ Because of their need to *feel something*.
- ▷ To have an *effect on others* or indicate distress.

What keeps them going?

- ▷ *Ambivalence*: Sufferers may not want help and often deny any problem.
- ▷ **Vicious Cycles:**
  - With *anorexia*, weight loss is accompanied by chemical changes, which affect the brain

and distort thinking. This makes it more difficult to get help or think rationally about food and weight.

- With *bulimia*, once a binge begins, people often describe feeling in a trance or a stupor; eating so quickly they don't even taste the food. They are then driven to purge — but hunger causes blood sugar drops that can trigger another binge.

▷ *Shame and Secrecy*: Sufferers often feel ashamed which leads to them lying about their behaviour or withdrawing from those who love them most.

▷ *Control:* Sufferers may feel a sense of control over their bodies by refusing food or purging — in fact, the longer the disorder lasts, the harder it becomes to resist.

The Cost

EDs seem to offer answers — but they strip you of all that matters: your health, your relationships, your time and *yourself*.

> "As EDs take hold, relationships with family members and loved ones become strained and gradually diminish."

Physical affects can include the following: dehydration, muscle atrophy, paralysis, gastrointestinal bleeding and ruptures, chronic fatigue, diabetes, kidney failure, osteoporosis, arthritis, cramps, bloating, incontinence, hair loss, gum disease, insomnia, hyperactivity, infertility, seizures and heart attacks.

Psychological affects: loneliness, exhaustion, despair, guilt, paranoia, anxiety, isolation, panic attacks and depression. Even semi-starvation produces significant increases in depression, hysteria and paranoia.

Relational: As EDs take hold, relationships with family members and loved ones become strained and gradually diminish. Attempts to help, often lead to further conflict and stress.

Key Point

EDs seem to offer life, but they take it from us instead.

1 Kings 18:16-29; Nehemiah 9:1-21, Galatians 4:1-9,
John 8:33-6.

5. Hungry hearts

And Jesus answered them, "Those who are well have no need of a physician, but those who are sick. I have not come to call the righteous but sinners to repentance." (Luke 5:31-32)

For whatsoever overcomes a person to that he is enslaved. (2 Peter 2:19)

EDs can cause serious physical and emotional damage, but they start in our hearts. This means that they are *spiritual problems,* needing spiritual as well as physical healing. We see this in Luke 5:17-26, when a paralyzed man comes to Jesus for help. We might think that his greatest need is to be made physically well, (and it's certainly a serious one!) But Jesus says there's something even more important. Before He deals with our bodies, He deals with our hearts. Here's why.

For sufferers, EDs can sometimes function like a religion. Like most religions, they are built on beliefs about what constitutes life and death, salvation and sin, shame and redemption. They tell us what it means to be human, what gives us identity and what we should *worship*. They have their own rules and rituals and they promise to rescue from "sin." Yet compare the laws of EDs to the real good news.

In the gospel, sin is about rejecting Christ and refusing to receive from a giving God. With EDs, sin is about falling short of my own standards and desires. Where the Bible points us to Jesus for salvation, EDs point us to food or our own self-will. Where the gospel tells us we're helpless and enslaved, EDs tell us that we can fix ourselves.

At the centre of the Christian faith is Christ's body, broken for us. This body speaks of grace and it pays the price. At the centre of the ED is another body, also broken. This body is mine and I have to save it. My ED promises liberation but no amount of food brings fullness. No amount of purging can make me clean.

The gospel of EDs isn't good news at all. It is a system of works, of slavery, self-salvation and self-destruction. It promises heaven, but delivers hell. It is a religion, as powerful and addictive as any cult.

What's the solution?

We need to be careful here. EDs are all about "solutions" and "self-improvements." They're all about us — our rules, our strength, our gospel, our way. EDs say, "Try harder, do more, make it better. Fix your own mistakes — or face the consequences." Gospel repentance is very different. It's not about anything we can do. It's about what Jesus has already done.

Key Point

EDs act like religions: they promise redemption but lead us into sin. Jeremiah 10:14, Proverbs 5:23, Proverbs 13:19, Proverbs 28:26, Psalm 115:1-18, Colossians 2:16-3:4.

6. Living bread

Jesus said to them, "I am the bread of life; whoever comes to me shall not hunger, and whoever believes in me shall never thirst. (John 6:35)

Jesus offers healing to those whose lives are dominated by food. But He comes as a doctor for *all* who are sick. This sickness is much more than what goes into our mouths. It's about trying to make life work without God. This is why Jesus dies. On the cross, He pays for *all* of the ways we try to feed and fix ourselves.

EDs are powerful and persuasive. They tell lies that can become our identity and for sufferers, they often feel like a friend. If we're going to let this "friend" go, we need something — someone — more beautiful to take its place.

The puritan Thomas Chalmers makes exactly this

point. He says that it's not enough to try harder to make ourselves better. If we want to change, we need a new and greater love; Jesus. When we know Him, we can say "no" to the things that have always enslaved us. When we know *Him*, we can count everything else as loss, (Philippians 1:21).

> "Saying 'no' to an ED feels like losing a part of ourselves."

Jesus sees us in all of our mess, but instead of walking by, He joins us in it. The Creator of the universe has pledged Himself to us — body and soul — and on the cross He is broken for us. Torn apart like bread and poured out like wine, He gives Himself so that we might be fed — and filled.

Saying "no" to an ED feels like losing a part of ourselves. It's frightening to challenge familiar behaviour and it's hard to break old habits. But don't despair. Jesus isn't calling us to change for change's sake. Nor is He asking us to do it because it's "good" for us, (like some kind of spiritual "spinach"). Jesus calls us to follow Him because this is how we find life in all of its fullness. EDs promise life and easy answers — but then deliver misery and death. Following Jesus means dying to who we were; but then discovering all that we were made to be.

> *For whoever would save his life will lose it, but whoever loses his life for my sake and the gospel's will save it.* (Mark 8:35)

The gospel isn't about trying harder or being more moral. It's acknowledging that we can't save ourselves, but Jesus can. We are hopeless sinners — but made perfect in Him. As we look to Jesus, we become more like Him. Instead of living in the shadow of our old selves, we live in the new identity that He has given us.

> *Therefore, if anyone is in Christ, he is a new creation. The old has passed away; behold, the new has come.* (2 Corinthians 5:17)

When we come to know Jesus, it's not that we no longer sin — but the power that sin held over us is now broken.

We'll still be tempted to go back to old patterns and old slaveries. But Jesus gives us His Spirit who helps us in our weakness. He gives us the motivation to change and the power to do so.

> *For those who live according to the flesh set their minds on the things of the flesh, but those who live according to the Spirit set their minds on the things of the Spirit.* (Romans 8:5)

In Christ we can start to say "no" to old desires, not because we want to be accepted, but because we *already* are.

Key Point

We cannot justify ourselves. But Jesus has done it for us.
Romans 5:1-11, Romans 10:9, Ephesians 2:1-10,
Philippians 3:1-11, Titus 3:1-7

7. Walking in freedom (self-care)

Then they said to him, "What must we do, to be doing the works of God?" Jesus answered them, "This is the work of God, that you believe in him whom he has sent." (John 6:28-9)

We have seen how disordered eating reflects something deeper, namely our disordered desires. If this is true then walking in freedom will mean more than just eating sensibly again. With Jesus' help, it will mean re-ordering our lives and learning how to live.

Here are a few practical ideas on how to do this. They're not the solution. But if you're determined to get better, they might help.

Get into the community. Get as much support as you possibly can — from your church, your friends, self-help and support groups and other professionals. When

> "Your doctor is the gateway to lots of other help — and it's important to be medically monitored."

you're going downhill, you can't always spot it, so make a "warning sign" list and share it with some close friends. This gives them permission to help when you stumble. Don't be afraid to suggest how others can pray or help, often they want to, but need direction on how.

Go to your GP. Your doctor is the gateway to lots of other help — and it's important to be medically monitored. *Bring a friend*, especially if you find it difficult, also think about making *a list of questions and things you'd like to cover.*

Keep a prayer journal. Use words, poetry, and art — anything to express yourself in ways that don't involve food. Pour out your heart to the Lord — and ask Him to help you.

Keep a diary of when, why and where you starve, binge or purge. Work out how you will deal with triggers, (e.g. by talking to friends or journaling when you feel the urge to overeat). Keep a record of every victory and learn from your mistakes.

Soak in the gospel. E.g. sermon podcasts, worship music and reading the Bible with another person. His truth will help you to fight the lies.

Take it step by step. Jesus tells us to pray for daily bread (Matt 6:11). He'll help us, a day at a time.

Break big goals into smaller ones. Examples include: limiting binges to one place and time, or gradually widening your diet if you only eat certain foods. If you purge, practise delaying until you can resist it entirely. Start with five minutes, then ten, then twenty and so on. Don't give up, it takes time and practice.

> "Soak in the gospel... His truth will help you to fight the lies."

Stick to a schedule. Set times of the day for each meal and snack. Make sure you're drinking plenty of fluids, as hunger and thirst can be easily confused. Don't fast or skip meals, as this will cause your blood sugar to drop and set you up for a binge. This is much less likely when your body knows it will be fed regularly with a variety of foods.

It may take several weeks or months before your appetite returns and in the early days you might feel bloated or unwell, but it's just your body getting used to normal feeding. In the meantime, *don't compensate* in other areas, e.g. by over-exercising or using laxatives/ slimming aids. If you do, talk to your doctor about cutting down and ultimately stopping.

Reclaim your time. Try to avoid unstructured time, especially in evenings or weekends. Plan a timetable of activities that aren't based around food and which you enjoy, such as volunteering — but give yourself plenty of rest.

Eat Mindfully. Find a quiet space where you can eat without distractions and when possible, eat with others. Give yourself a clear cut-off point for the end of the meal, then leave the table or go into another room. Pray about how you're feeling.

Don't trust your feelings. Fighting an addiction is difficult and sometimes you will feel rotten! Focus on what you are achieving, rather than on what you will lose. What does your ED stop you from doing? What would life look like without it? Be specific — the friends you'd

> "We are weak, but Jesus is stronger than any enemy or fear. He is in control, though we are not…"

see, the places you'd go. Write them where you can see them. This is what you're moving towards.

Don't write off your feelings. Our emotions don't tell us who we are, but they are a part of who God has made us. It's okay to be frightened — but God is greater than our fears. It's natural to want to be in control — but God can be trusted.

Remember who you are. You are not your ED, no matter how long it's been a part of your life. You're a child of God — chosen, accepted and dearly loved. You don't need to feel it for it to be true!

Remember who Jesus is. When you resist an ED, you may feel anxious and agitated. Don't panic. We are weak, but Jesus is stronger than any enemy or fear. He is in control, though we are not, (see Mark 4:35-5:43).

Struggling is part of recovery, but thoughts don't have to lead to actions. Just as we learn negative ways of thinking, we can learn positive ones too. For example, instead of telling yourself "I've overeaten and I want to purge," replace it with, "I want to purge — but that's okay. If I don't give in, nothing terrible will happen. The desire will get weaker and in time, it'll go away."

"Remember that the longer the eating disorder goes on, the more it captures our hearts. There's no better time for recovery than today."

Be practical. If you struggle with binging, practise leaving a little food on your plate. If you tend to overeat in a certain place, try to eat somewhere else and focus on each mouthful. Don't go food shopping when you're overtired, hungry or have had an emotional shock. Make a grocery list in advance or order online. Avoid trigger foods where possible and pack foods away so you don't always see them.

Don't give up. Recovery is hard but in Christ we can do it. Just because you've tried and failed in the past, doesn't mean you can't do it this time round. Start again and keep going — it's a process and we learn from our mistakes. Remember that the longer the eating disorder goes on, the more it captures our hearts. There's no better time for recovery than today.

Key Point

Jesus calls us to leave behind things which enslave us- and He gives us the power to do so. In Him, we are made new.
Isaiah 43:18-19, Jeremiah 32:17, Mark 8:34, Romans 12:1-2, 2 Corinthians 5:17, Hebrews 4:16, Revelation 21:5

8. Feeding others

For I was hungry and you gave me food, I was thirsty and you gave me drink, I was a stranger and you welcomed me, I was naked and you clothed me, I was sick and you visited me, I was in prison and you came to me. (Matthew 25:35-36)

How to help

It's tempting to think that since EDs come under "mental health," only qualified experts can help. This is not the case! You can't force a person with an eating disorder to change, but you can encourage them to seek treatment and be there for them as they seek to recover. You can pray for and with them, cheer them on, keep them company and hope for them when they can't hope for themselves. Most of all, you can gently point them to the

Saviour who sets prisoners free, (Luke 4:18).

Myths about EDs

▷ **They only apply to one type of person**. No - EDs affect all ages, genders and ethnicities and each person experiences them differently.
▷ **There's only one kind and it's obvious which.** EDs don't fit neat categories and there can be crossover between them. For example, up to 60% of recovering anorexics struggle with bulimia. Bulimics often employ "anorexic" strategies like starvation, to try and lose weight.
▷ **Appearance as portrayed in magazines**, (extreme weight loss). No - with bulimia for example, sufferers are usually around a normal weight. Most of the damage can be hidden/ internal.
▷ **They're about feeling "fat"**. This may be a symptom, but the cause is much deeper.
▷ People with EDs **don't like food**. Even if they

don't eat much, they're usually obsessed by it.

▷ **One ED is "worse" or "better" than another.**
They're all distressing.

▷ **If someone gains or loses weight, they're
recovered.** EDs start in the brain, long before
the behaviours — so recovery is about more than
just body mass. Challenging your ED means
losing a familiar coping mechanism — recovery
is the time when sufferers need more help and
not less.

▷ **If sufferers say that they're ok, then they are.**
Denial is a feature of most EDs.

▷ **EDs are "caused" by single traumatic events.**
Not always! Most EDs are the result of many
different factors - and some of these can look
entirely ordinary.

▷ Those with EDs will always **hide their weight.**
Some will, but some will draw attention to it.

▷ **Binge eating is just greed**. No. It's about
emotional hunger and relief using food e.g. as
reward or comfort or distraction.

> **Sufferers can't be helped.** It takes time and effort — but you can make a difference.

The Common Fears of Sufferers:

> "I'm not thin enough. They won't believe me."
> "They won't think it's an Eating Disorder — they'll just think I'm fat"
> "People won't take me seriously."
> "They'll take this too seriously. They'll tell others, lock me up and take away control."
> "The doctor will just try to make me gain/lose weight!"
> "I'm too old/young/wrong gender/wrong size to have an eating disorder."

Don't

> Think you're unqualified to help because you're not an ED expert. By all means involve ED "professionals", but remember that your own

ministry of praying and listening is vital.

▷ Ignore weight OR focus solely upon it. Matters of the heart are at least as important, but body and mind are closely linked. Avoid unnecessary comments about food, appearance or weight. Ask open questions like: "How are you feeling?" or "How's your day been?" rather than "What did you eat for lunch?" or "Have you just made yourself sick?"

▷ Assume that weight gain or loss means the sufferer is better — this is when they will need more support rather than less.

▷ Get drawn into their world. It's very easy for disordered patterns or thinking to be normalized.

Do

▷ Make sure that *you* are grounded in Christ and supported by His people.

▷ Where possible, work alongside families and

medical professionals.

▷ Read up-to-date information on EDs.

▷ Acknowledge your own feelings — even if they're mixed. It's natural to hate the disorder, but be careful about venting frustrations on sufferers.

▷ Be prepared for a range of reactions, from anger to denial. Make sure sufferers know *you are available to chat* if and when they feel ready - and offer practical support e.g. accompanying them to see their GP.

▷ If you're concerned about a child, *make a list* of the things that are worrying you. For example: skipping meals, being anxious while eating and rituals such as dividing, weighing and playing with food, sudden changes in diet (e.g. becoming vegetarian to avoid eating), going straight to the bathroom after meals. *When* did the behavior start? What sort of *physical and emotional changes* have you noticed? How does your child talk about his or her body? Have others commented? For example, teachers or friends? Talk about your concerns with your GP or health worker.

▷ Don't waste time blaming yourself or others - you may never know what triggered an ED. Instead *focus on what you can do and on opening up a conversation* with the sufferer.

▷ Gently remind sufferers of the ways in which their life will improve with normal eating. Offer to go shopping with them and plan/prepare meals ahead of time. Routine will often help sufferers feel safer, especially in the early stages of recovery.

▷ Provide long-term support. Recovery can take months or more usually, years and relapse can be a part of it.

▷ Be sensitive- don't base all your activities/church events around food.

▷ Provide extra help during times of transition, (e.g. from hospital to home).

▷ Offer to stay with the sufferer and help out with

siblings, so that parents/carers can have a break.

▷ Treat the person with an eating disorder as you did before they got sick. Remind them that they are valued and valuable e.g. by helping them to use their gifts, (especially in small and non-pressurised environments).

▷ Speak of Jesus and His grace — the gospel really is the best medicine.

▷ Remember you are not the Saviour, Jesus is. He comes for the lost (Luke 19:10) — and no one is beyond his help.

Key Point

We can't rescue those with EDs, but we can love them and point them back to Jesus. John 13:12-17, 34-35, Galatians 6:1-5, Philippians 2:1-11, Hebrews 10:24-25, 1 John 4:7-8

9. Daily bread — how to keep going

And I am sure of this, that he who began a good work in you will bring it to completion at the day of Jesus Christ. (Philippians 1:6)

You are not your eating disorder, no matter how long you've had it or how bad you feel. Even if you don't know who you are, Jesus does. He has plans for you and purpose and hope. This is part of the reason that He puts us in communities because we cannot do life alone. So don't be afraid to *ask for help*. God has made us to depend upon one another and having needs is part of being human.

Be patient. Sometimes, you'll feel angry or sad or overwhelmed or unsafe or crazy. These feelings are not the truth and they will pass. Your circumstances will change. Suffering has a "used by" date and there is hope. Only *Jesus'* future is forever. You *will* feel better.

Recovery does not mean waking up one day and suddenly finding that all of your old struggles have disappeared. But you are ready for it — and there's no better day to start than today. Remember that *you can recognise ED thoughts and feelings, without acting on them*. And you can learn healthier ways of coping, just as you learned unhealthy ones. This will take time and effort, so give *yourself permission to make mistakes*.

As part of your recovery, there may be times when you may fall back into old patterns. When this happens, *resist the urge to give up or condemn yourself*. Remember: "The steadfast love of the Lord never ceases, his mercies never come to an end; they are new every morning great is your faithfulness." (Lamentations 3:22-23). Instead, *learn from your mistakes*. What was it that made you want to go back to old behaviour? What could you change for the next time?

Guard your heart by avoiding what is harmful (e.g. diet books or unhelpful websites or literature) and by filling your minds with gospel truths (e.g. by memorising Bible verses that challenge old lies).

Look to Jesus

Read Job 16:19-21. Notice the four titles of Jesus:

▷ **Witness:** Jesus sees all that goes on. Nothing is hidden from him. Nothing is wasted. You are not anonymous or invisible to the King of Heaven.

▷ **Advocate:** You may feel completely out of your depth. But you have an advocate in heaven - someone who speaks and acts for you when you can't do it for yourself.

▷ **Intercessor:** Maybe, you feel like you can't pray. Even so, Jesus prays for you. He pleads for you, as one pleads for a friend - even when you're too tired to speak.

▷ **Friend:** Perhaps you feel unlovable and alone. Jesus sees you - exactly as you are. He longs for you to pour out your heart to Him. He carries you and He leads to a place of rest.

Remain in Christ: Read John 15:4-5. Jesus is in control of every detail of our lives. This means that we can rest, knowing we are safe in His care. Every day we go back to the cross for forgiveness, strength and grace — and every day His mercies are new!

Stay focused: Because recovery is hard, doesn't mean it's impossible. Just because you've tried before and relapsed, doesn't mean you can't do it now. It's a process and it will take time. But the more you try it, the more likely you are to succeed. The battle is won in lots of baby steps, not one great leap.

Keep trusting: God's not about replacing us, but renewing what's there. So don't put limits on what He can see and accomplish in us. "Impossible? Miraculous?" That's what He *does*. That's what He's doing in *you*.

Key Point

Recovery is a process; but Jesus is with us every step — and He will bring us through. Psalm 27:14, Romans 8:18-39, Ephesians 6:10-18, Philippians 3:14, Philippians 4:13, Colossians 1:11-12, 2 Tim 1:7, James 1:12